DEAR GRANDAD

from you to me®

A JOURNAL OF A LIFETIME

Dear

This journal is a gift with a twist . . . it's from you to me.

When we are children we are always asking questions . . . well now I have some more for you. Please could you answer them in the way that only you know how and then give the book back to me.

There might be a couple of questions that you would prefer not to answer, so don't worry, just answer the others as well as you can . . . I won't mind.

People say that we all have at least one book in us and this will be one of yours. The story of you and me that I will treasure forever.

Thank you,

with love

Tell me about the time and place you were born . . .

What are some of your earliest memories?

I'd like to know about your parents . . . names, dates of birth and tell me some stories about them . . .

Tell me what you know about your mother's parents and family . . .

Tell me what you know about your father's parents and family . . .

Please detail what you know of our family tree . . .

What interesting information do you know about other people in our family?

Here's some space for you to add more about our family that will interest generations to come . . .

What do you remember about the place/s you lived when you were a child?

What were your favourite childhood toys or games?

What sort of pets did you have when you were young and what were their names?

What do you remember about your holidays as a child?

What did you do for entertainment when you were young?

What did you study at school / college and what were you best at?

Tell me about the things you did as a child that are different for today's children . . .

What did you want to do when you grew up?

What were your favourite hobbies when you were young?

Did you have an idol when you were young?
Tell me who and why . . .

What was the first piece of music you bought and in what format?

What chores had to be done when you were young that aren't needed to be done today?

Describe any family traditions you had or maybe still have . . .

What age were you when you started work?

Tell me about the jobs you have had . . .

How did you meet my grandmother?

What would you do for a night-out when you were dating?

Tell me about a memorable piece of music that you and my grandmother had 'just for you' . . .

Describe a special day you had with my grandmother . . .

Choosing the names for your children can be really difficult . . . how did you decide?

Tell me what my mum / dad was like when they were younger . . .

I would love to know more about my parents . . .
what else can you tell me?

How did you feel when you were told you were
going to be a grandparent?

What did you think when you first met me?

In what ways am I similar or different to my mum / dad?

Can you see any characteristics in me that come from other people in our family?

Describe some of your favourite memories of the times we have spent together . . .

Describe what you like about me . . .

Is there anything you would like to change
about me?

Tell me about the friends you have had in your life . . .

What piece/s of music would you choose to be in your 'top 10' favourite tracks?

Tell me about the most interesting places you have travelled to . . .

What are the happiest or greatest memories of your life?

What are a few of your favourite things?

Describe your memory of some major world
events that have happened in your lifetime . . .

Describe the greatest changes that you have
seen in your lifetime so far . . .

Do you think life today is better or worse than when you were young? How is it different?

Who or what has been the greatest influence on you?

If you were an animal . . . what type of animal would you be, and why?

If you won the Lottery . . . what would you do with the money?

What have you found most difficult in your life?

What regrets do you have in your life?

Can you do anything about them now?

Tell me about the things that have made you happy or laugh . . .

With hindsight what would you do differently?

Describe something you still want to achieve in your life . . .

Tell me something you think I won't know about you . . .

How do you like to be thought of by others?

Given your experiences, what advice would you like to offer me?

And now your chance to tell me some other
personal stories that you want to share . . .

These extra pages are for us to write any questions, memories or answers that may not have been covered elsewhere in the book . . .

AND FINALLY FOR THE RECORD . . .

What is your full name?

What is your date of birth?

What colour are your eyes?

How tall are you?

What blood group are you?

What date did you complete this story for me?

THANK YOU

for taking the time to complete this journal.
I will treasure it forever.

DEAR GRANDAD

from you to me®

The Timeless Collection, first published by **FROM YOU TO ME LTD** in September 2017

There are nine titles in the collection:
Dear Mum, Dad, Grandma, Grandad, Daughter, Son, Sister, Brother and Friend.

For a full range of all our titles where gifts can also be personalised, please visit

WWW.FROMYOUTOME.COM

FROM YOU TO ME are committed to a sustainable future for our business, our customers and our planet. This book is printed and bound in China on FSC®certified paper.

7 9 11 13 15 14 12 10 8 6

Copyright © 2017 **FROM YOU TO ME LTD**

ISBN 978-1-907860-33-1

FROM YOU TO ME LTD, STUDIO 100, THE OLD LEATHER FACTORY
GLOVE FACTORY STUDIOS, HOLT, WILTSHIRE, BA14 6RJ

ISBN 978-1-907860-33-1